X 3525

All rights reserved

This 1994 edition published by Grange Books

An imprint of Grange Books PLC

The Grange, Grange Yard, London SE1 3AG

© *1994 Loveline Publishing*

CONCEIVED BY *Waterbridge Books*

DESIGNED BY *Chris Humour*

EDITED BY *Virginia Comfrey*

TYPESET BY *Chris Lanaway*

Photographs © *Loveline Publishing*

Printed and bound in Italy

ISBN 1-85627-483-7

THE *Lovers' Guide* TO
SENSUAL MASSAGE

THE *Lovers'* GUIDE TO
SENSUAL MASSAGE

Grange
BOOKS

Introduction

*R*esearching into the history of massage is like discovering a see-saw of emotion because this seems to be an emotive subject surrounded by mystery – some societies welcomed the art, others were afraid of it and treated massage as evil.

It is also interesting to discover the way massage grew in prestige in the ancient world and declined in esteem during the Middle Ages only to revive again in the twentieth century. In fact, when one reads the history of massage, it serves as a window through which one can see the types of society at any given period. For instance, at the height of any religious fervour, massage was regarded as decadent; in societies that had a more enlightened attitude it was accepted and its benefits recognised.

Both the Greeks and Romans were obsessed with the 'body beautiful' and arranged games, gymnastics and competitions in large arenas to show off their best examples of healthy manhood. These superb athletes became the élite who were

given their own handmaidens to bathe and massage them so that their muscles and skin would glow with good health.

There are many other historical records of the use of massage and it is interesting to see how little the practice has changed despite the advance of science and the introduction of many mechanical aids.

Massage promotes a feeling of well-being and the use of oils and creams was introduced to beautify, soften and give a therapeutic effect to the skin and muscles. Gone are the days when people thought of massage as an indulgence. Scientists now realise the potential of massage and have discovered that it releases powerful natural pain killers in our bodies. With more and more emphasis being placed on fitness and health, massage becomes less the treatment for the wealthy, the athletes and the professional dancer and more a part of a keep-fit routine for all people concerned with maintaining a fit and healthy body.

What is Massage?

*M*assage, correctly given, offers relief from muscle strain This is because when a muscle is massaged, blood is expelled from the area and when pressure is removed, fresh, newly oxygenated blood flows into the muscle, thus improving its tone. Tension is lessened by slow, rhythmic stroking, allowing the recipient to relax.

Friction and pressure improves circulation to the viscera and the skin develops a more glowing and healthy appearance.

All these results of massage ensure a more flexible and invigorated body.

Just as with many other forms of treatment, massage must not be given to people suffering from certain conditions or disorders, such as contagious or infectious skin conditions, thrombosis, phlebitis, angina pectoris, hypertension, varicose veins or any unidentified lump or swelling. In pregnancy, the abdomen should not be massaged.

Massage is therapeutic; it can be tantalising, sensitive or sensuous - it is all up to you. You can make it fun, for it should be enjoyed. This Guide introduces you to the delights of sensual massage, and allows you the chance to learn how to bring pleasure and relaxation to friends and partners.

The History of Massage

The art of massage has been practised by many cultures over the centuries and it is fascinating to read of the many uses it served. For example, mention was made of athletes being massaged before the Olympic Games in 776 B.C. It is also interesting to discover the way massage grew in prestige in the ancient world and declined in esteem in the Middle Ages only to revive again in the twentieth century.

It has taken many forms. In Babylonian and Assyrian cultures, massage was used with drugs, hot and cold poultices and douches. Archaeologists working in Asia Minor have found oils and perfume phials dating back to early civilisations which had been used in ritual demonstrations.

In ancient Egypt, the Pharaohs were anointed and massaged as a symbol of their royalty, and even in death they were massaged with embalming oils for their journey into the 'other world'.

It is thought that the Chinese were giving massages 2,700 years before the birth of Christ. Mention of the art was recorded in one of the oldest medical works: The Yellow Emperor's Classic of Internal Medicine.

Since 600 B.C. when Hinduism first evolved out of the Vedic religion, Hindu brides have been massaged with herbs and oils prior to their wedding, and to ward off evil spirits.

One of the founders of modern massage techniques was the Greek physician, Galen (A.D. 129-199). He classified massage into three qualities ('firm,' 'moderate' and 'gentle') and three quantities ('little', 'moderate' and 'much'). By different combinations he arrived at nine different forms of massage, each of which had its own specific indications.

The word 'massage' was not used until the 19th century when it appeared in a French-German dictionary of 1812. Before that the Greek word tripsis or the Latin word frictio, or the national equivalent, was used by writers on this subject.

In ancient documents the words 'rubbing', 'squeezing', 'pressing' or 'the laying on of hands' were recorded and friction and exercise were always linked.

An English textbook written in 1866 was entitled The Anatriptic Art. Whilst these words continued in use until the turn of the century, the new French terms were gaining acceptance in many countries in the Western hemisphere. The French also named the different movements in massage, adding to the ancient word of 'friction'. These are now commonly known as 'effleurage', 'petrissage', 'tapotement' and 'vibrations'.

Although they have developed it to a fine art, massage was around long before the French discovered it.

Making your own Massage Oils

If at all possible, try mixing your own body oils using six drops of essential oil to ten millilitres of vegetable oil. Given below are just some of the variations you might like to try.

BASIL: Refreshing, uplifting and very good for mental fatigue.

CEDARWOOD: Has a harmonising nature that helps stabilise unbalanced energies.

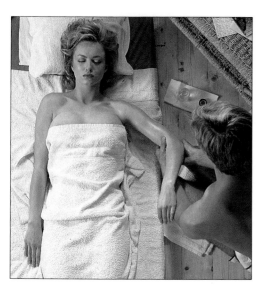

CLARY-SAGE: A good general tonic.

CLOVE: Dispels physical and mental fatigue.

FRANKINSENCE: The original 'incense'.

JASMIN: Rich floral scent; euphoric and strong sensual stimulant.

LAVENDER: Antiseptic and a splendid restorative for mental and physical exhaustion; one of the most useful and popular oils.

LEMON GRASS: An uplifting, sweet, lemony scent.

LINDEN BLOSSOM: Relieves tension; a good oil to massage with before sleep.

MARJORAM: Good for insomnia; its herbal scent has a strong calming effect.

MYRRH: Healing and rejuvenating.

ORANGE: Uplifting and refreshing.

PEPPERMINT: Cooling and good for sunburn.

ROSE: A good revitalising tonic.

SANDALWOOD: Provides a quietening and meditative effect.

YLANG-YLANG: A sweet, exotic scent from the Middle East; revitalising and good for the sympathetic nervous system.

Keep mixed oils in dark glass jars. Store them in a cool, dark place.

Techniques and Movement of Massage

*T*his book uses non-technical words wherever possible and limits the movements to the five basic ones listed below.

◆ Effleurage (Figure 1)
This is the first and main movement and is a stroking, gliding movement. It is executed with the flat of the hand and precedes all other movements. Stroking is done towards the heart and the pressure should be slow and rhythmic, firm on the upward stroke but light on the downward.

◆ Petrissage (Figure 2)
This is a squeezing movement, usually circular, and is applied with the thumbs and/or fingers. It is mainly carried out over soft tissue that has bone immediately beneath it. This movement must be performed without sliding the hands.

◆ Cupping, Hacking, Pounding (Figure 2)
These movements, intended to promote circulation, are carried out on the back, shoulders and thighs.

Cupping is performed by keeping the palms arched and the fingers slightly arched but relaxed. Keep the wrist flexible and aim for a 1,2:1,2 tempo: like the sound of a horse trotting.

Hacking uses the sides of both hands, but the fingers are kept relaxed and slightly curved. This movement is usually given on the back, shoulders, backs of the legs and buttocks. The tempo is the same as for cupping.

Pounding involves clenching the hands to form a fist and then beating lightly in the same tempo as for cupping. It is most beneficial over the lung area and the buttocks but the site of the kidneys should be avoided.

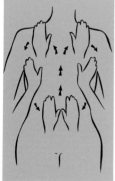

figure 1

figure 2

◆ *Arm Massage*

KNEEL facing your partner and apply
a small amount of oil to your hands.
Now effleurage up your partner's right
arm, from the back of the hand to the
shoulder. (**1**, **2**, **3**). Repeat three times.

HOLD the forearm with your
right hand and with the thumb and
fingers of your left hand, work up the
outer part of the upper arm from the
elbow to the shoulder with small
circular pressures. Repeat three times
(**4**, **5** and **6**).

REPEAT this movement on the
inside of the upper arm using your
right thumb and fingers to massage.
Repeat three times.

WITH the palms of both your hands roll up the upper arm. The tempo should 1, 2, 3 up and 1, 2, 3 down. Repeat several times (movements **7** and **8**).

WITH the knuckles of your fingers move up the side of the lower arm from wrist to elbow. Repeat three times (movement **9**).

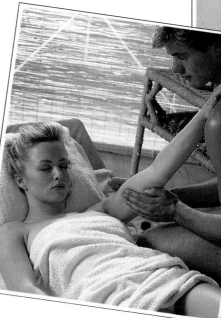

STROKE the whole arm again from the hand to the shoulder and back. With the thumb and first finger of both your hands hold your partner's thumb and small finger and begin small circles over the top of the fingers working to the end of the fingers and thumb. When you reach the middle finger, hold the wrist with your left hand and complete the massage of the middle finger (movements **10** and **11**).

TAKE hold of the little finger by the first knuckle, near the top of the finger and give a small pull. Repeat for each finger and the thumb.

TURN the hand over and press the palm with the heel of your hand with circular movements (**12**).

FINISH off with the first movement. Come back to the hand with slightly increased pressure on the little finger and thumb.

13

NOW, massage the top of the foot with the full flat of the right hand. Use your left hand to hold the foot. Repeat three times.

WITH the thumb of both hands work up the spaces between the toes, towards the ankle. Repeat three times, slowly.

HOLD the foot firmly and press it towards the ankle and then rotate it one way, then the other way. Hold the heel and grasp the toes and gently pull the leg. With your hands

◆ Leg and Foot Massage

KNEEL down facing your partner. Apply a small amount of oil to your hands and then stroke with a broad sweep from the top of the foot, right up to the thigh and return. Your right hand should be positioned on the left side of the foot and your left hand on the right side of the foot, and when you reach the thigh your hands cross over and return down the leg back to the foot with the left hand pulling the big toe. Repeat three times (**13**, **14**, **15** and **16**).

clenched, slide them up the
outside of the lower leg to the
knee, and return with a stroking
movement with the hands open.
Repeat three times (**17**, **18** and **19**).

BEND your partner's knee and
with the fingers of both hands
rhythmically 'hit' the calf muscle
starting from just above the ankle up
to the back of the knee. Repeat three
times (**20** and **21**).

PLACE the leg back in the
resting position and with both hands
above the knee smooth round and
under the knee. Repeat three times.

WITH the flat of both hands on the top of the thigh just above the knee slide up the thigh and when you reach the groin press lightly and return your hands back to the starting position. Repeat three times (**22**).

WITH the knuckles of both hands stroke up the inner and outer thigh and return to the knee with the hands open. Aim at an even tempo. Repeat three times (**23**).

CHANGE your position and kneel to the side of your partner, facing sideways, and hack up to the top of the thigh from just above the knee. Repeat three times (**24**).

NOW cup hands with the fingers closed but relaxed and bring the hands down alternately on to the top of the thigh. Work up and down and incorporate the inner thigh. Repeat three times (**25, 26**).

END the leg massage by repeating the effleurage movement right up the leg and by pulling on the big toes, gently squeezing at the last stroke. Repeat on left arm and leg.

25

26

◆ Abdomen and Rib Cage

KNEEL facing your partner and with a small amount of oil on your hands sweep across the midriff and under the waist then pull gently from the spine back along the pelvis to the front of the abdomen. Repeat three times (**27**, **28**, **29** and **30**).

WITH your thumbs on the right side of the lower abdomen, slowly massage up the ascending colon, then across the top of the transverse colon and down the descending colon. Repeat this movement several times and each time slowly increase

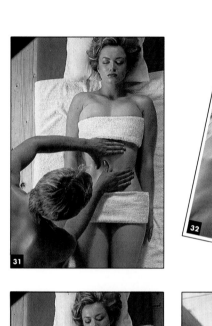

the pressure. With the heel of the
hand describe circles and use gentle
pressure over the same area, exactly
as before. Repeat three times. Finish
off with the first stroking movement
(**31**, **32**, **33**, **34** and **35**).

MOVE up to the chest area and
position yourself at your partner's
head. With the fingers of both hands,
circle chest wall from the centre of

37

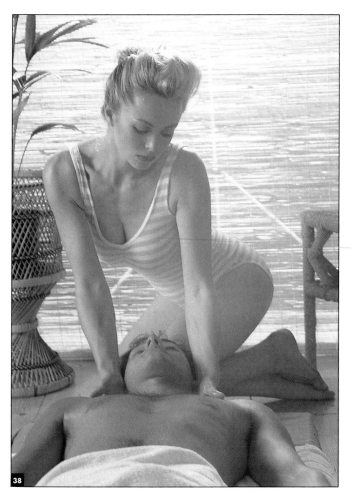

the sternum out towards the shoulder. When you reach the shoulders turn your hands with the palms facing you and with your fingers on the back of the shoulders. Massage along the shoulder line to the hairline, then press hard on the back of the base of the skull. Repeat several times (**36**, **37**, **38** and **39**).

NOW, proceed with the back.

◆ Feet and Legs - Back

PUT a small pillow under the ankle. With a very small amount of oil on your hands, massage down the sole of the foot with the heel of your hand for several movements. On the last movement, press firmly and circle each toe with the thumb of your right hand holding the foot in your left hand. Repeat the toe massage three times (**40**).

MOVE up to the heel and massage by grasping the heel with the whole hand, and your thumb pointing

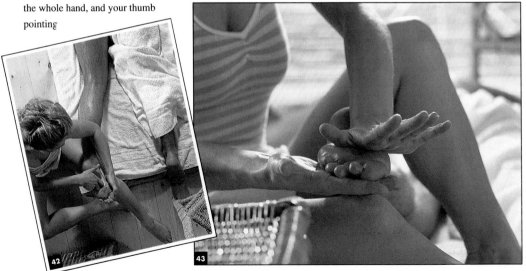

towards the toes. Finish off the foot
with knuckle stroking down the
sole of the foot. Use strong, firm,
slow movements (**41**, **42** and **43**).

WITH the palms of both
hands just by the ankle, slide
your hands right up the whole
leg from ankle to thigh and
return to the ankle. Repeat
three times (**44** and **45**).

NOW, with the knuckles of
both hands move up from the
ankle to the knee, on the
outside of the lower leg.
Repeat three times.

NOW move up to the thigh and repeat the same movements as for the lower leg after you finished the side knuckle movement. Repeat this to the centre of the thigh, over the hamstring muscles (**46**, **47**, **48** and **49**).

MOVE to the side of your partner and with your hands in a karate position, hack from the top of the thigh to the ankle and back. Do not hack over the back of the knee. Work slowly in the 1,2:1,2 tempo

and proceed up and down the whole leg several times. Finish off at the top of the thigh (**50**).

MAKE fists and pound on the top of the thigh moving slowly down to the ankle in the same manner as the hacking movement. Remember not to hit the back of the knee. Finish off at the top of the thigh (**51**).

FINISH off the leg and foot massage with three large, sweeping, stroking movements from the foot up the entire leg returning with a firm hold on the toe.

◆ The Back

WITH your hands lightly oiled, begin at the base of the spine. Slide up to the neck and sweep your hands out across the shoulders. Move down the outside of the back to the waist and then sweep out over the hips and buttocks back to the commencement of the stroke. Repeat this three times (**52**, **53**, **54**, **55** and **56**).

MOVE up from the base of the spine to the shoulders with the same movement. At the outer shoulders, make a circular movement with

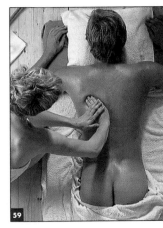

your fingers to the centre of the neck. Repeat three times. With your right hand on the back of the neck squeeze slowly up the neck to the hairline. Press firmly on the occipital bone with thumb and fingers. Slide back to the base of the neck. Repeat this movement slowly and rhythmically.

NOW, move out to the left shoulder and with the karate movement hack along the shoulder line. Do this three times

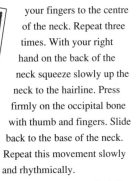

on the left side then, without breaking the movement, continue over on the right shoulder (**57**).

WITH the fingers of the right hand on the left shoulder by the neck and your left hand resting on top of your right hand make circular movements out towards the arm. Move your fingers down the outside of the shoulder blade coming in towards the spine and back up to the start position. Repeat three times, ending up by the neck, and then

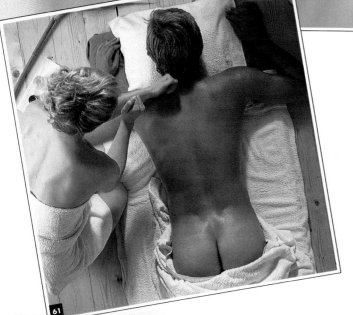

61

62

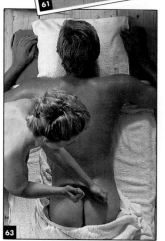

63

work out over the right shoulder in exactly the same manner. Finish the movement at the centre of the neck (**58**, **59** and **60**).

FORM your hands into fists and pound across the shoulders, down each side of the spine to the buttocks using more pressure for the buttock area. Continue up and down for several movements and finish off at the buttocks (**61**, **62** and **63**).

FORM hands into the cupping position and work up and over the buttocks and back with vigorous and rhythmic cupping movements.

Repeat three times (**64** and **65**).

FINISH off at the buttocks and then, with the knuckles of your right index and middle fingers, slide up each side of the spine to the top of the neck (**66** and **67**).

WITH both hands, press firmly down the back, close to each side of the spine. Your fingers should point outwards and you should work down towards the buttocks.

FINISH off with the effleurage movement, three times.

COVER your partner and allow them to relax.

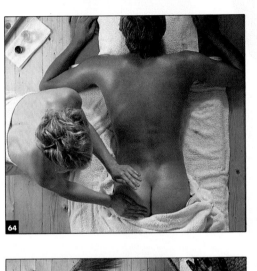

64

66

65

67

◆ *Electric Hand Massagers*

WHEN using these machines, the following rules must be observed. Because of the heat generated by the electric massager, talcum powder must be used on the body at the commencement of the massage and the machine should only be used for a maximum of ten minutes and then rested and allowed to cool down. Change the massage heads to suit different parts of the body.

◆ *Arm Massage*

BEGIN by stroking the talc up the arm. Gently place the massager on the forearm just above the wrist and circle up the arm. When you reach the upper arm move your left hand further up to support the upper arm (**68**, **69**, **70** and **71**).

LIGHTLY glide back to the start position and begin again.

MASSAGE the upper arm first on the inside, then from the centre up to the top of the arm, finishing on the outer plane of the arm from the elbow upwards. Massage rhythmically and always upwards towards the heart.

◆ Leg Massage

REMEMBER to change the massage
head to a stronger one. (Various
kinds are supplied with the
machine.) Talc the leg from the
ankle to the top of the thigh. Ask
your partner to bend their knee and
now begin on the outer side of the
lower leg from just above the ankle
bone up to the side of the knee.

RETURN to the ankle and repeat
the movement three times. Move the

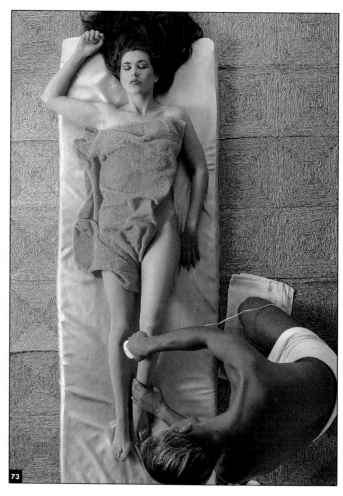

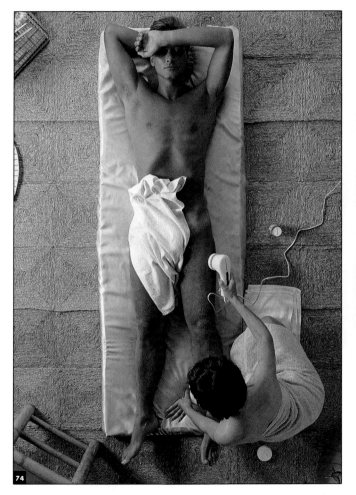

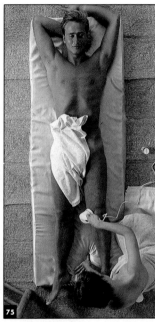

massager to the inner calf and repeat the movement (**72** and **73**).

STRAIGHTEN the leg and move up to the thigh. Begin on the outer side of the thigh, from the side of the knee up to the top of the thigh. Repeat this movement three times and then move to the inner thigh and continue as before.

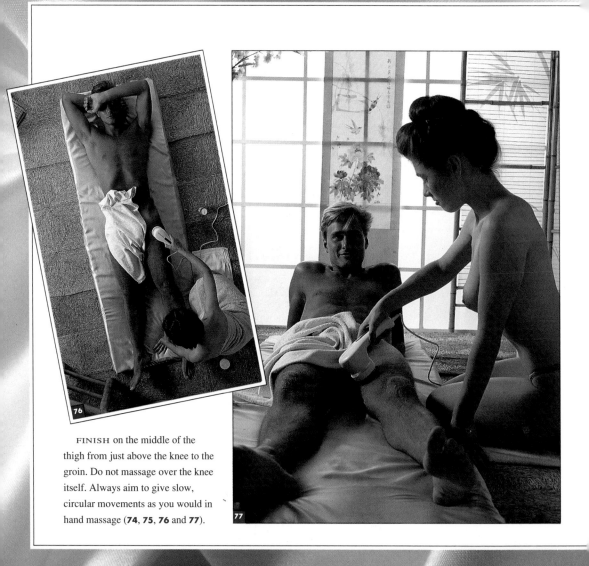

FINISH on the middle of the thigh from just above the knee to the groin. Do not massage over the knee itself. Always aim to give slow, circular movements as you would in hand massage (**74**, **75**, **76** and **77**).

◆ Abdomen Massage

CHANGE the head of the massager to a soft sponge applicator and talc your partner's abdomen.

BEGIN at the bottom right hand side and gently follow the ascending colon, work along the transverse colon and down the descending colon - in fact, follow the digestive tract. Remember to keep a steady pressure (**78**, **79** and **80**).

◆ Chest Massage

FIRST apply talc then, using the same applicator head as for the abdomen, move across the upper chest working in circles from the middle of the chest out to the left and back to the middle and out to the right. Go over the area three times, finishing on the right shoulder (**81**, **82**, **83**, **84**, **85** and **86**).

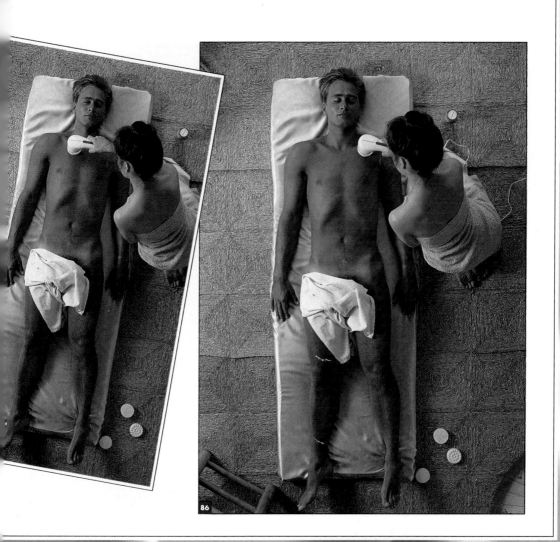

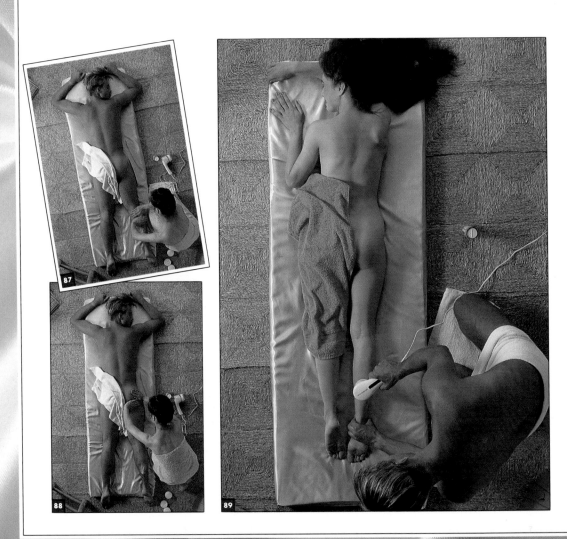

◆ Leg Massage - Back

CHANGE the massage head to a hard stimulator, talc the leg.

START just above the ankle. Move over the back of the calf muscle up to the back of the knee. Glide the massager back to the start. Repeat three times (**87** and **88**).

CONTINUE up the leg to the outer thigh, then the inside thigh, finishing off on the centre of the thigh, working up the hamstring muscles to just below the buttock.

REPEAT three times (**89**, **90**, **91**, **92** and **93**)

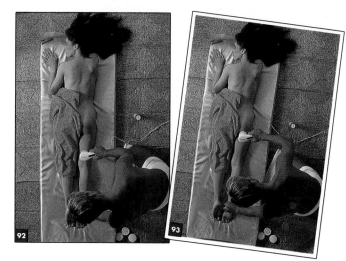

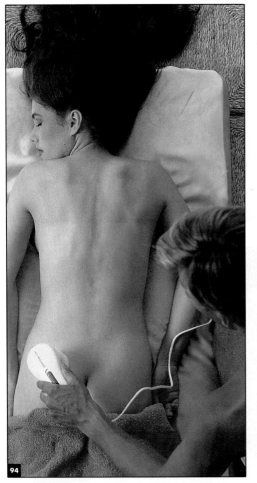

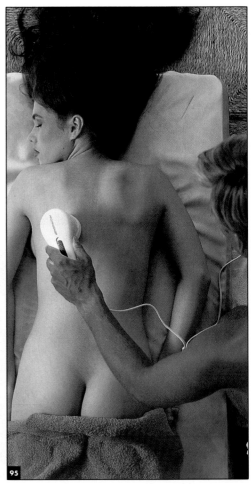

94

95

◆ Back Massage

TALC the back and work up one side of the back from the buttock to the shoulder and repeat on the opposite side. Begin the massage with the hard applicator but after working the back three times, change to a soft applicator and spend a little longer working on the shoulder and neck area to ease out the stress and tension which accumulates in this area (**94, 95, 96, 97** and **98**).

◆ Head Massage

A SPECIAL spiky applicator head is used for this type of massage. Do not use talc. Work over the scalp in circular movements from the base of the skull up one side of the head to the hairline and begin again on the other side of the head working from the base of the skull to the hairline.

WHEN you have finished using the massager, clean the heads thoroughly with warm, soapy water and dry well. Do not use dirty applicator heads on another person as they could be carrying infectious skin diseases.

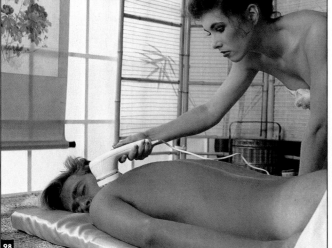

Facial Massage

Facial massage is extremely helpful for the over-tense and nervous individual and is a good way to begin a full body massage. It eases headaches, releases tension and can help drain sinuses and relieve puffy eyes. If you do not have time to give a full massage, the facial massage will be just the thing to relax and refresh your partner.

◆ Pre-facial Treatments

To get the maximum benefit from a well-executed facial massage, prepare the skin beforehand.
If you are going to be massaged, thoroughly cleanse your face paying particular attention to the crease in the chin and the sides of the nose. Follow with a facial sauna. If you do not have a facial sauna machine you can still carry out the next stage with a kettle of boiling water. Pour the water into a basin and allow it to fill to a depth of about three inches. Throw in a handful of herbs – either

sage, peppermint, camomile flowers, marigold petals, or lavender flowers. All of these herbs have either healing properties or smell nice, or both. Cover your head with a towel and hold your face in the steam for at least ten minutes. Towel dry and remove any blackheads. Then apply a mask treatment suitable for your skin type. There are many different types on the market, but it is fun to make your own and it costs very little (whisked egg white is a wonderful pre-party treatment as it leaves the skin glowing). While relaxing with your face mask, use cucumber to take down swellings from the eyes. Grated potato in gauze also helps to draw out inflammation around the eyes.

◆ The 12-step Massage

If there is time, try the pre-facial treatments first. At least make sure the face is free of make-up and the day's accumulation of grime. Apply

a small amount of massage cream or oil to the face and neck, working from the neck up to the forehead.
1. START with the hands at the centre of the forehead. First the right hand glides from the forehead and before it reaches the hairline the left hand follows the same movement. Let the hands follow in a continuous movement and use gentle but firm pressure. Work three movements in the centre, move out to the left side, work three movements, back to the centre and out to the right side, work

100

three movements. Finish the movement again in the centre of the forehead (**99**).

2. TURN the hands, fingers together, facing towards the nose and smooth out across the forehead to the temples. With the middle finger of

both hands, press into the temple, hold the pressure to the count of three and then release the pressure and return to the centre of the forehead.

With the hands in the same position, pull up the forehead from

the eyebrows towards the hairline. Work first to the left side of the forehead, then to the right and finish back at the centre. Repeat the movement three times and finish at the centre of the forehead (**100**, **101** and **102**).

3. INTERLOCK your fingers so that the middle finger of your right hand is placed between the first and middle fingers of your left hand and circle across the forehead from left to right, finishing in the centre. Turn your hands, fingers together, facing

the nose and smooth out to the temples and hold the pressure, then release (**103** and **104**).

4. WITH the ring finger of both hands, work small circles from the outer corners of the eyes in towards the nose; turn the hands and bring

the fingers lightly up the side of the nose and apply a slight pressure at the junction of the nose and eyebrow. Repeat three times, finishing finally at the centre of the forehead and smooth out to the temple as before (**105** and **106**).

5. BRING your hands down to the left hand side of the face and with the two middle fingers of each hand slowly work over the jawline from outer mouth to ear. Repeat three times. Lift the muscles and feel them respond to pressure (**107** and **108**).

6. CONTINUE up the side of the face in a line from the side of the nose out towards the middle of the ear. Finish off the movement by the

109

110

left temple, move the right hand across to the right temple then apply pressure and release (**109** and **110**).

7. BEGIN the same movement on the right side, finishing off at the right temple, bringing the left hand across the forehead to the left temple and applying pressure as before.

8. PLACE your thumbs on top of the chin and circle over the chin to the count of three. Now, work around the mouth with both thumbs until you reach the centre of the top lip. Break off the movement and return to the chin and repeat smoothing the

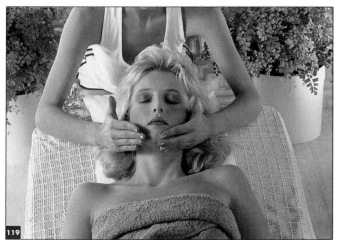

mouth and easing out the strain. Finish off at the centre of the top lip and bring hands down to underneath the chin and then circle out along the jawline towards the ears. This area gets very tense and a slow pressure helps to ease the strain. Repeat three times (**111**, **112**, **113**, **114** and **115**).

9. FINISH off below the ears and then massage the neck with broad round strokes. At the base of the neck, drop your hands over the chest and make large circles ending at the back of the neck. You should end

the hairline and gently lift the cheekbones with the two middle fingers of each hand. Move in towards the nose. Repeat three times and end by the nose (**122** and **123**).

11. SLIDE up the nose and, with both thumbs on the opposite sides of the nose, circle the sides of the nose and then bring your thumbs to the top of the nose and circle up the nose to the top of the forehead. Your thumbs, when you change from the side of the nose to the top, will be in the correct position to circle up the

this stroke at the back of the neck, into the base of the skull. Now, bring your hands back to the jawline by the ears, and begin to tap lightly along the jawline starting at the left-hand side and working along to the right-hand side and back again. The movement should be a light tapping with the finger tips, first the left hand, then the right hand, in a 1,2;1,2 tempo. End the movement under the chin (**116**, **117**, **118**, **119**, **120** and **121**).

10. SLIDE your fingers out to the ears and then up the cheekbone by

nose and over the forehead.

At the top of the forehead, slide the thumbs out to the temple and press and release temple pressure as before (**124**, **125** and **126**).

12. MOVE your hands, with your fingers extended and your thumbs to the back of the head, over the hair and slowly circle the head with increasing pressure (**127**).

Finish off the massage with forehead stroking movements in exactly the same way as you commenced the facial and gently ease off at the third stroke.

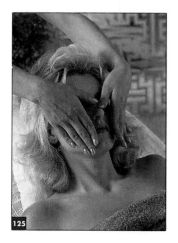

125

126

127